Diana Kimpton
Illustrated by John Haslam

Ruby was an artist.
She loved red.
Even her cat was red.

Sky was an artist.
He loved blue.
Even his hair was blue.

One day, Ruby and Sky were eating breakfast.
Ruby had toast and red jam.

Sky had blueberry muffins.

"This room is dull," said Ruby.
"Let's paint it!" said Sky.

“Yes!” said Ruby. “Let’s paint it red.”
“No!” said Sky. “Let’s paint it blue.”

Ruby got some red paint.
She started to paint the wall red.

Sky got some blue paint.
He started to paint the wall blue.
They went faster and faster.

“Yuck! Look at that red wall,”
said Sky.
He painted some blue stripes.

“Yuck! Look at that blue wall,”
said Ruby.
She painted some red spots.

The blue paint ran into the red paint.

The red paint ran into the blue paint.
The wall went purple.

"I love it!" said Ruby.

"It's cool!" said Sky.

"Purple is just right," they said.